C000261945

Incubation at Home

by

Michael Roberts

Illustrated by
Sara Roadnight

Edited by *Richard Roadnight*

Cover Photograph
Newly Hatched Chicks by **Richard Roadnight**

Copyright Michael Roberts 1996

Published by Domestic Fowl Research

Printed by Quorum Technical Services Ltd,
Unit 3, Lansdown Industrial Estate, Cheltenham, Glos. GL51 8PL

ISBN 0 947 870 16 4

HISTORY

Artificial incubation has been practised since early civilisation. When man became settled, there was a need for a more continuous source of protein. Until then, most protein had come from the seas and rivers, and hunted animals, birds and reptiles. As hens and ducks reproduce so quickly in egg form, man domesticated them, and this has led to the multi-million pound businesses of today.

Hearson's incubator circa 1920

HEARSON'S
Champion Incubators
THE ORIGINAL AND STILL THE BEST

THE 100% HATCHERS

THEY ARE SAFE INVESTMENTS

ORIGINAL STANDARD MODELS WITH COPPER TANKS					NEW MODELS (of Lighter Construction) WITH COPPER TANKS				
No.	Egg Capacity				No.	Egg Capacity			
2.	25/30	..	£6 10	0	06	50/60	..	£6 15	0
6.	50/60	..	£8 10	0	011.	100/120	..	£8 10	0
11.	100/120	..	£12 15	0	016.	150/180	..	£11 15	0
20	200/240.	..	£19 15	0	020.	200/240	..	£16 10	0

No.	TUBULAR WATER HEATED MODELS						
71.	300 Egg Capacity, 2 drawers separately controlled					£26 10	0
91.	600 ,,	,,	4	,,	,,	£42 0	0
93.	1200 ,,	,,	8	,,	,,	£72 0	0

Man contrived various methods of incubating eggs in different parts of the world, the most fascinating of which has been used for thousands of years, and can still be seen today in the **Fayoum** area of **Egypt**. This consists of a building about 70 feet long, 60 feet wide, and 16 feet high. It is constructed of sun-dried brick, and has 12 alcoves.

There were different systems to be found in China and the Philippines, but in Europe it was not until 1750 that a Frenchman called **Reaumur** hatched some chicks by placing the eggs in a barrel surrounded by rotting horse manure. The Australian **Mallee bird** uses the same principle, incubating its eggs in huge piles of soil and vegetation. In 1770, **John Champion** from Berwick-upon-Tweed developed a system that passed warm air through a box containing the eggs. By 1777 another Frenchman called **Bouneman** was using warm water pipes. Incubators progressed from fairly primitive methods into scientific machines in the 1800s. In 1844 the first patent for an incubator was taken out in England – this used a charcoal fire to heat water. By now the race was on: all kinds of cabinets were developed, with doors and drawers, heated by candles, gas, paraffin and charcoal. Many were marketed with over zealous sales patter according to the individual manufacturer. There were simply scores of makes, and even today there are dozens of manufacturers world-wide. Most incubators now are electric, for compactness, lightness and practicability. The differences in the mechanisms for turning eggs

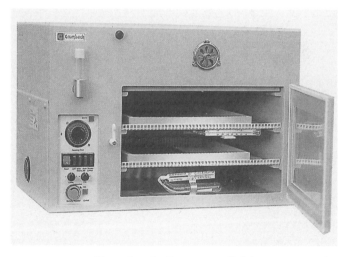

Grumbach Compact S 84

have always interested me – some roll the eggs, some rock them gently and others involve turning the whole machine from side to side.

There will continue to be a never ending quest to find the ideal incubator, but, as you will see in the following chapters, the perfect incubator in the wrong place will not produce perfect results.

Brinsea Octagon 20

INCUBATORS

Incubators come in all sorts of shapes and sizes, but there are two main types: still-air or fan-assisted.

STILL-AIR INCUBATORS

These incubators have a thermostatically controlled heating element, which is normally above or at the side of the eggs. Some smaller incubators use a bulb, but most have a flexible heating cable. The air in a still-air incubator does not remain static, but circulates slowly, and leaves the incubator by convection. There is always a drop in **temperature** if you turn the eggs by hand, but the **heat** soon builds up when you replace the lid or drawer. These incubators normally have more insulation in order to hold a constant temperature, and are better if power cuts may be a problem.

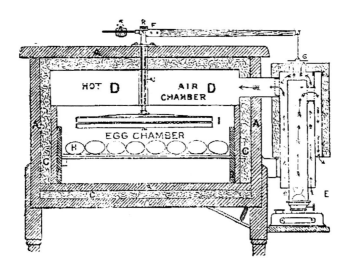

Still-air incubator

FAN-ASSISTED INCUBATORS

All large incubators and some smaller ones are fan assisted. These incubators are similar to the previous kind, but have a fan incorporated, normally at the top or side. This forces or assists the air round the machine, ensuring an even flow of warm, thermostatically controlled air round the eggs. These incubators normally have less insulation pro-rata than still-air machines, and are particularly at risk where there are power cuts. When buying a **second-hand** machine, check that the fan is working.

Both kinds of incubator can be liable to hot and cold spots if not designed properly; the chicks hatch earlier or later, or not at all in the warmer or cooler areas.

Brinsea Polyhatch incubator

KIT FORM INCUBATORS

These are excellent value, if you are a good enough carpenter to build them from a kit. You get instructions for making a box to house the heating element, etc. They normally come in 4 sizes: 25, 50, 75 and 100 egg capacity.

POLYSTYRENE INCUBATORS

Polystyrene incubators are cheap and work well, but this particular material is impossible to clean and sterilise properly – this always leads to a build up of **bacteria**.

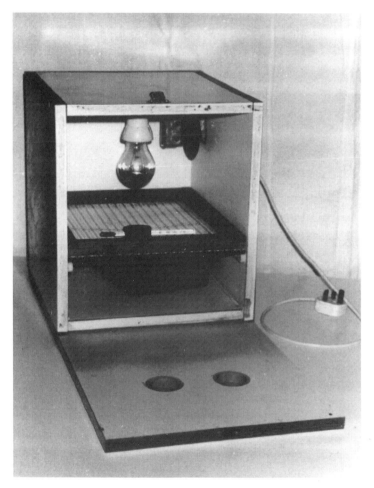

A home made incubator

LIST OF INCUBATOR MANUFACTURERS

AB Incubators Ltd.
40 Old Market Street, Mendlesham, Suffolk IP14 5SA

Brinsea Products Ltd.
Station Road, Sandford, Avon B19 5RA

Bristol Incubators
Latteridge Lane, Iron Acton, Bristol BS17 1TY

Brower Incubators
PO Box 2000, Houghton, Iowa 52631, USA

Curfew Incubators
Buttons Hill, Southminster Rd., Althorne, Essex CM3 6EN

Ecostat
Bosleake Ind. Est. Carn Brea, Redruth, Cornwall TR15 3YG

Grumbach Bruterate GMBH
AM Breitteil 2, Munchholzhausen 6330, Wetzlar, West Germany

Humidaire Incubator Co.
PO Box 9, New Madison, Ohio 45346, USA

Lyon Electric Co. Inc.
2765 Main St., Chulavista CA 91911, USA

Kuhl Corporation
Kuhl Road, PO Box 26, Flemington, New Jersey, USA

Ovolux/Humblet Spri
BP 500, B4000, Liege, Belgium

Petersime Incubator Co.
300 North Bridge Road, Gettysburg, Ohio 45328, USA

Masalles C/-
Balmes 25, 08291 Ripollet, Barcelona, Spain

Natureform Inc.
925 North Ocean Street, Jacksonville, FL 32202 USA

Miller Manufacturing Co. Inc.
South Saint Paul, Minnesota, USA

S. Broedmachines
   Margarethastraat 32, Ittervoort, Holland, 6014
Werner Schumacher Ing
   Landenbach, Oberhessen, West Germany
Victoria
   Via Lardirago 4, 27100 Pavia, Italy

A Russian incubator

THE

"TRIUMPH"

INCUBATOR

The World's Best and British Made.

For Catalogue and Further Particulars, apply to:

WILLIAM LEA,

Royal Appliance Works,

BIRKDALE, SOUTHPORT.

CATALOGUES FREE AND POST FREE.

16

PREPARATION

This is one of the most important chapters concerning incubation.

CLEANING AND STERILISATION

If you have bought a new machine, there is no need to sterilise it. If you have borrowed or bought a **second-hand** machine, take it to pieces as far as sensibly possible, and clean and sterilise it. Use a sponge and proper sterilising agent, for example VIRKON S. Milton from Boots will do but it is corrosive. Soap powder, bleach, etc., are not effective against chicken **bacteria** and pathogens. Do not soak the electrical or electronic parts, but wipe away surplus water with kitchen paper, then allow to dry and put the machine together. Do this after each hatch, otherwise you could lose a setting due to a build-up of germs. Incubators are the most splendid machines for the growth of bacteria!

Sterilise in a clean area, and ensure that you only use sterile materials.

LOCATION

This is where a lot of people come unstuck. The commercial world uses specially designed rooms, varying in size from small to vast, which are carefully monitored for **temperature** and humidity. In the home this is obviously not practical, but these conditions must be mimicked as far as possible.

The ideal place is a dry cellar, or brick built garage or outhouse. What you are looking for is a room where the temperature is constant. A spare room will do, as long as the temperature is fairly even, but keep the incubator away from the door, radiators and windows.

You avoid windows mainly to minimise draughts and changes in temperature, but I have a theory that **light** can affect hatchability. I have no direct evidence for this, but it is a subject that interests me: eggs incubated naturally under their mother or under a broody are nearly always in the dark. If you use an incubator that has a large see-through glass or PERSPEX cover it may be worth taking special care to avoid direct sunlight.

Some people use a dehumidifier to reduce the humidity in the room. Make sure you have access to two or three nearby electric sockets – most automatic turning machines have two plugs, one for the heater, the other for the turning mechanism: it is handy to have a third for candling. Put coloured insulation tape across the plug, to stop anyone from removing it.

It is important that you put the incubator on a secure table or bench, so that it cannot be accidentally nudged or bumped into.

I have known of cases where people get fantastic hatches early in the year and poor results later on using the same regime. The atmosphere in the location, (apart from being blue!) can change! I have also known of incubators being moved from one end of the room to the other with dire results, so if you find a good spot, don't change it.

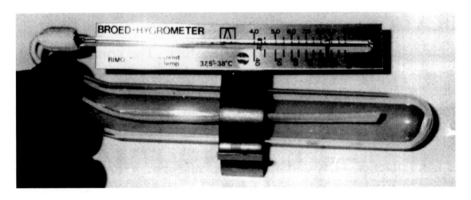

Broed hygrometer, a wet bulb thermometer

THERMOMETERS

This is the next important item. Do not use one thermometer, but two – thermometers can be inaccurate. In a still-air machine use a mercury-in-glass thermometer just above the eggs, so that it does not interfere with turning. For the check or second thermometer use a "Digital Strip Thermometer", on a plastic card – this needs to lie on top of the eggs. A maximum and minimum thermometer is good, as the needle inside will tell you of any temperature fluctuations, but it is not very easy to read accurately. The thermometer in a fan assisted incubator needs to be about 1½ inches or 3½ cm above the eggs. You need a **temperature** of 37.5 °C.

Try not to adjust the **thermostat** every time you check the incubator. You will find the temperature varies a little each time you look at the thermometer, record this.

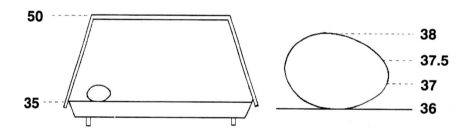

In still-air incubators the temperature may vary by as much as 15° between the bottom and top of the incubator, and by up to 3° between the top and bottom of the egg. It is important to place the bulb of the thermometer just above the eggs, with a temperature of 38.5°C.

HUMIDITY

This section is about how much water to use and when to add it. It is necessary to understand that when an egg is incubating it has to lose up to 14% of its weight in order to create a big enough air sac. The only way an egg can lose weight is by losing moisture. If you are adding too much water to the incubator, the egg can't lose the right amount of moisture. This leads to lack of air space, which in turn leads to fully formed chicks dead in their shell.

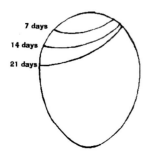

Growth of air sac

Very few of the small incubators have any humidity control, so adding water is a matter of good judgement and luck, as most manufacturers' instructions are very vague.

A study of mallards nesting at the Domestic Fowl Trust, reveals that they start their nest on the ground, and as the incubation period goes on, the nest becomes higher and higher. There must be a lesson to be learnt there.

So how do you know how much water to add? This utterly depends on where you live, how wet or dry your surroundings are, what altitude you live at, and the weather conditions at the time of incubation. This is where **record-keeping** comes into its own.

As a rule of thumb, put in half a cup of water at setting. Add no more until the day before hatching; then fill the trays. You may find that you will need no water to start off with, or a little water right the way through the incubation period. There is no hard and fast rule, and beware – you may need more water when incubating duck and goose eggs. You may also find that the amount of water you put in during February and March, will differ from May and June. So, as I always say to my customers: when using small incubators you may not get brilliant hatches with the first, second or third settings – by the fourth you will be getting somewhere near. To help you learn from your experience, read "WHERE DID I GO WRONG" on page 46.

Your incubator may have a **wet and dry bulb thermometer**, to measure the humidity. The wet bulb has a wick attached to it that looks like a tiny linen sleeve and must be kept clean at all times. The drier the air the greater is the evaporation and the greater the difference in the wet and dry bulb readings. A wet bulb reading close to the dry bulb reading means high humidity; a bigger difference (lower wet bulb reading) means low humidity. Consult your incubation manual, as small incubators with humidity controls tend to have fairly specific instructions.

If your incubator has this type of thermometer, always use a measuring jug to add water, and record how much you use.

RECORDS

It is imperative to keep records, not only the **temperature** and humidity inside the incubator, but of what is happening outside as well – for instance thundery weather can affect hatching eggs. Records are important because any slight variations you may make (amounts of water put in, hatching times, etc.) can affect the outcome. With the best will in the world you will not remember precisely what you did in the previous hatch. Records can be as detailed as you want, but the simpler the better. It is from your records that you will build up a knowledge of your machine, and the various different breeds of birds that you are hatching. You can make a copy of the record card for each hatch.

Incubator record card

DATE OF SETTING   QUANTITY BREED(S)

Day	Temp Inside	Humidity Inside	Room Temp	Weather	Turning Check					Notes: Water, Candling, Infertilities, etc.
1										
2										
3										
4										
5										
6										
7										
8										
9										
10										
11										
12										
13										
14										
15										
16										
17										
18										
19										
20										
21										
22										
23										
24										
25										
26										
27										
28										
29										
30										
31										
32										
33										
34										
35										

ELECTRICITY AND ALARMS

Most incubators use between 30 to 75 watts of power so the cost of running an incubator is minimal.

It is worth getting an electric alarm: the best type we use is a simple plug-in alarm, which informs you when the circuit or the electricity goes off. There is not much you can do if this happens, other than to have a portable generator at hand, but it might show you why a certain setting did not hatch. Also some circuit breakers or trip- switches are very sensitive, and can be triggered by a power surge, etc. Most incubators have a pilot light to indicate if they are on or off.

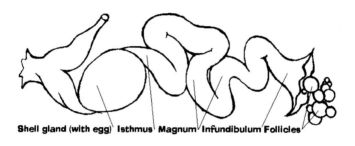

Shell gland (with egg) Isthmus Magnum Infundibulum Follicles

Hen's reproductive system

LAYING

First we must look at the source of the eggs: feed hens and cocks with the best food, before and during the time that you are taking the eggs for incubation. Increase the **protein** to 18%, add some vitamins and allow plenty of access to mixed grit. The occasional small tin of fish cat food once a month will help you to obtain good shaped healthy eggs. Be sure that your lighting programme is working: your birds will need 14 hours of **daylight**. Check for **fleas**, particularly the cockerels: they won't mate if they carry a flea burden.

NEST BOXES

Be sure these are always clean, with plenty of straw or shavings. Some modern hen houses have the next boxes above the perches – a bad design fault, as it results in the birds roosting in the nest boxes. This means the eggs will be dirty, and you will have to clean these nest boxes daily. Make sure ducks and geese have plenty of straw, as their eggs can be very dirty. You need to bring in eggs that are as clean as possible.

COLLECTION

When collecting your eggs, make sure that you do not bang or jar them, or leave them out in the sun. Collect them in a bucket or basket with fresh straw or shavings in the bottom, to prevent them rolling about and cracking. If you collect from different breeds with similar egg colour, mark the eggs as you collect them.

TO CLEAN OR NOT TO CLEAN

Eggs, particularly duck and goose eggs, are porous, and this allows them to breathe: handle them with care.

There are two schools of thought on cleaning, but if you have picked up clean eggs, there is no need to wash them.

Some people think that you should not clean eggs at all but pop them straight into the incubator, others think that you should wash all eggs.

I am a firm believer in as little cleaning as possible. There is no doubt that scraping, cleaning and washing eggs results in a loss of hatchability. Having said that, if you have dirty eggs, this is what you should do. Scrape off the thick mud or soil, with a clean knife and then place them in a bucket of warm water (35 degrees) with ½ teaspoon of VIRKON S, or other brand of egg wash. Wipe them with a clean kitchen scourer, and allow to dry on kitchen paper. Soak and wash eggs according to dirtiness, always leaving the dirtiest until last.

It is important to use clean eggs in your incubator: dirty ones will cause a build up of bacteria, which could spoil a setting. The dirty-egg brigade counter that if you clean and sterilise your machine after each hatch, there should be no problem. All the eggs from one hen will have some immunity to her bacteria; but in nearly all cases, the dirty eggs you put in your machine come from various birds, and possibly various breeds.

Once your clean eggs are dry, always handle them with clean hands or with rubber or plastic gloves that you only use for the incubation process. The 'Diesel gloves' found at petrol stations are excellent.

Ensure that you only use clean eggs and materials.

SELECTION OF EGGS

Having collected, and if necessary cleaned, your eggs, you need to select ones of the correct **size** and **shape**. Naturally, you will discard any that are misshapen, **double-yolkers**, (candle if in doubt) or eggs with poor shell quality. This only comes with experience, as there are so many differences in egg sizes, shapes and colours. For example: good Anconas' hatching eggs are large and chalky white, Marans' are good sized and as deep brown as possible, but Buff Cochins (which are huge birds) lay bantam size pinkish eggs. With ducks, Cayugas lay sooty black eggs, and all the Campbells should lay white eggs. With geese, Embdens lay huge white eggs, and Toulouse eggs are small by comparison, to name but a few differences.

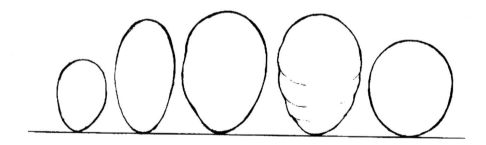

Mis-shaped eggs, unsuitable for hatching

Do not use cracked eggs. If you are unsure if an egg is **cracked**, gently knock it against another one, then knock together two sound ones – you will hear the difference between a good egg and a cracked one.

STORAGE

Always wait at least 24 hours before putting freshly laid eggs in the incubator – 3 days is best. You can incubate hens' eggs 1 to 10 days old, but the optimum time for **setting** them is between day 3 and day 7. Because the pores on duck and goose eggs are larger, the storage time is only 7 to 8 days. This is why you never see ducks' eggs for sale in supermarkets – hens' eggs can be several weeks old.

The easiest way to store eggs is to use clean egg trays or boxes, in a cool room or larder. Eggs are very susceptible to heat or cold during **storage**; an ideal **temperature** is 13-14°C. Use a brick or block of wood to tilt the tray or boxes to one side one day, and to the other side the next day until the eggs go into the incubator.

Another way to store eggs, (and again there are two schools of thought here), is to place the eggs on their side in a tray of dry sand, **turning** the eggs by hand. Don't forget to put a "+" or an "0" on either side of the egg, indicating which ones you have turned. The purists only use pencil to **mark eggs**, but a felt-tipped pen will do. (See turning).

TRANSPORT

If you are sending duck, hen, turkey, goose or bantam eggs, place them in boxes of six, **packed** in kitchen paper. If the cardboard box has a hinged top, and the eggs are so tight that you cannot close the box, cut off the top and hold it on the box with rubber bands. The eggs must be firm inside. Put the boxes into plastic bags so that, if there is a leak, it does not contaminate the other eggs and the carrier will not arrive with a dripping box! Close the plastic bags with wire ties.

Stage 1

Stage 2

Stage 3

Stage 4

28

Stage 5

Stage 6

Stage 7

Stage 8

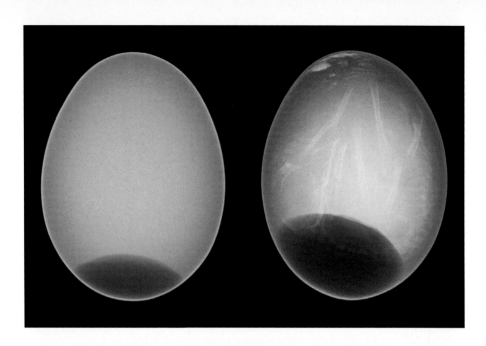

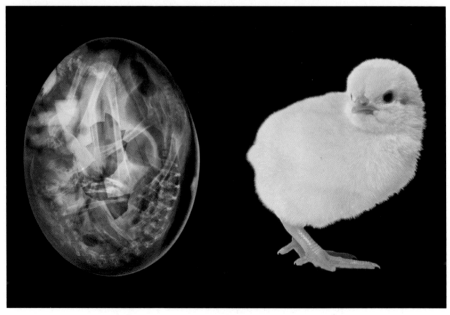

X-rays of chick development inside an egg

Commercial egg candling

Egg candling in Egypt using a box candler

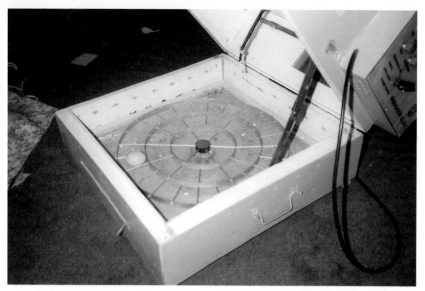

A fascinating Russian incubator. The 'wheel' rotates backwards and forwards to turn the eggs. Note the different sized spaces for the eggs on the outside and those on the inside.

Chicks hatching

Week-old coloured turkey chicks

Pomeranian goslings. These were the first to be imported
from America.

Pack the small cardboard egg boxes in a larger box: a light wooden one is best, as a cardboard one can get crushed. Pack the egg box or boxes with wood shavings so that they are firm inside the wooden box. Mark clearly with 'EGGS' or 'GLASS'. I have sent eggs all over the world like this, even through the post, and normally they arrive intact. **Hatchability** will depend on how much jarring and banging about they get, and on **temperature** fluctuations during the journey.

When you receive eggs, unpack them and leave them quiet for 24 hours before putting them in an incubator.

Curfew RX200 incubator

INCUBATION

TEST AND WARM UP

To check that the **turning** mechanism is working, set up the machine, put in an egg with numbers or different marks round the middle, and bring the incubator up to temperature. Run the incubator empty (except for the turn- checking egg) for a couple of days, noting and recording the temperature.

If you are new to the incubation process it is a good idea to try out your machine on less important breeds before you start on the rarer or more expensive ones.

SETTING

Now the incubator is set up, everything is working and ready for the eggs. When you put in the hatching eggs, the temperature in the incubator will plummet, but will come back up after an hour or so. You may need to adjust the **thermostat** a little. Don't forget to add a measured and recorded amount of water and pop in the digital thermometer.

With experience and good hygiene, you can have more than one batch or setting in your incubator. Setting weekly lets you set all your eggs between one and ten days old, and ties in well with the weekly candling routine. For details see "Storage" on page 26 and "Checking Egg Development" on page 36. **Mark** your eggs in some way so you know when they should hatch.

If you have an automatic turner, there is nothing more to do but carry out your daily recording, and checking your wet and dry bulb thermometer according to the manufacturers' instructions.

TURNING EGGS

Most incubators have automatic turning devices: some rock the eggs, some roll them on rollers or on a moving floor. In Russia I saw an incubator with a round floor: It rolled the eggs between small bars like the spokes of a wheel – and the spokes were cunningly constructed so that the inside eggs rolled the same distance as those on the outside.

To most people, an egg consists of a yolk and surrounding white, but it is, in fact, quite a complex thing. Imagine the yolk floating in the albumen (or white), held in place by a string or chalaza at each end, like a kind of "hammock", see the diagram.

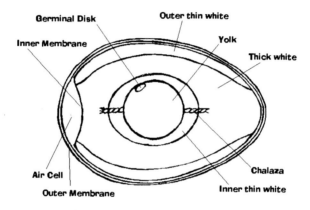

Cross section of an egg, showing the chalaza

You must turn the eggs first one way then back again: do not turn them in the same direction each time. If you roll the eggs continuously one way, it has the effect of tightening the strings of the "hammock", and thus constricting the embryo inside.

Some people are concerned by the heat loss when hand turning eggs in a non automatic turning incubator. This does not affect them, as a fertile egg holds its temperature. An infertile one loses heat rapidly – this is how a hen knows when to kick an egg out of the nest. Some people recommend a daily cooling period during incubation; no harm is done providing the eggs are not without heat for longer than half an hour.

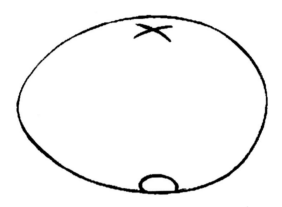

Egg marked for checking turning

Most machines turn the eggs about 8 times in 24 hours. You should do it either 3 times a day, after each meal, or 5 times a day – that is, once when you get up, once after each meal and once before you go to bed. The odd number is essential so that the egg never rests on the same side for two consecutive nights.

Don't forget to wash your hands before touching the eggs.

CANDLING

In the old days, eggs were checked in bowls or buckets of warm water; the **infertile** eggs sank, and the fertile ones "bobbed", or half sank according to the development in the egg.

Candling is a method of checking the progress of the development of the chick. It is called "candling" because originally candles were used to shine light through the egg in a dark room.

Early electric candlers had a bulb in a wooden box with a hole for the beam of light. To-day we have progressed to hand-held electric candlers, which you place against the "blunt" end of the egg. The advantage of these hand-held candlers is that you do not have to touch the egg, cutting down on transmission of **bacteria**.

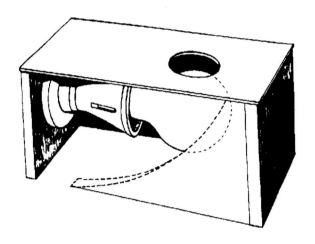

A simple home-made candler

It is more difficult to see into dark-shelled eggs. Candling in subdued light helps, as do candlers with bright bulbs. High efficiency bulbs, for example halogen, produce more light without a proportionately high heat output. To prevent the heat harming the embryo, do not leave the candler against the egg for any length of time – you only need a few seconds.

When candling, avoid unplugging the incubator heater – if you do not have separate sockets for heater, turner and candler, use the turning mechanism socket.

Candle weekly, see "Checking Egg Development" below, and pull out the clear or **infertile** eggs. This is particularly important for duck and goose eggs, as infertile, or "died during development" ones, become potential "bangers", and can ruin the entire setting.

CHECKING EGG DEVELOPMENT

Day seven is the first **candling** day. The embryo looks like a large red spider, with a red blob in the middle – this is the heart, and you should be able to see it beating. There should be a clearly defined air sac, and the egg should be dark and cloudy. **Clear eggs** have a poorly defined air sac, the egg lights up with the light behind it. When you candle the egg on its side the yoke floats around, always coming to the top of the egg – pull out any clears. Most eggs that appear freckled are infertile.

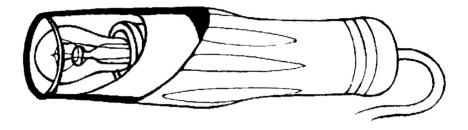

A modern hand-held candler

Day fourteen is the next candling period. Pull out any eggs that have not progressed. If you are incubating hens and bantam eggs, candle again on day nineteen.

If you are incubating duck and goose eggs, you need to candle again on day 21 and again on day 24.

When you candle eggs near to hatching, you will see the chick move its head away from the light. Look for signs of **pipping** – the chick trying to peck through the shell.

Sometimes eggs may get **cracked** a few days before they are due to hatch – this not the same as early pipping. You can save the egg and chick inside by painting over the cracked area with a little clear nail varnish.

Call duck eggs pip on day 25/26 and large ducks and geese on 27/28. The day before hatching remember to turn off the rolling mechanism (or stop turning the eggs) and increase the **humidity**.

The reason for the sharp increase in humidity is to ensure the chick is unrestricted inside the egg and can turn round to get out. If the egg is too dry the membrane round the chick shrink-wraps it. See "HUMIDITY" on page 19.

You should end up with some chicks, but do not be too surprised if there are only a few – you are on a learning curve. If you do not get good results, see "WHERE DID I GO WRONG" on page 46.

The Development of a Fertilised Hen's Egg (21 days)

It is not intended to go into the exact chemistry and physiology of the development of the **embryo**, but only the formation of the embryo as seen under a microscope. The stages of development as listed below would vary according to species and incubation time.

Day 0   In a **fertilised egg** there is always a small white spot near to the edge of the yolk: this is the germinal disk.

Day 1   The start of the development of the brain and nervous system.

Day 2/3   The start of the development of the heart and blood vessels, and the head. The heart will start to beat and the blood circulate.

Day 4/6   The eyes start to form and there are nodes which are the beginnings of wings and legs. The embryo, which looks like a cashew nut and has an over large head, envelopes the heart which started life outside the body.

Day 7/8   Other internal organs start to develop.

Day 9/10   Claws, legs, wings and beak are now clearly visible.

Day 11/12   Feathers start to appear.

Day 13/20   The body grows into proportion with the head and the embryo starts to take up the prenatal position, with the chick sitting in the pointed end of the egg. The neck is curved round its body with the head under the right wing. The head is poised to enter the **air sac**, and the feet and legs are drawn closely up to the body.

Day 21   The **hatching** process.

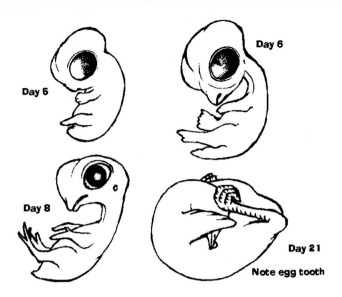

Developing chick embryos

Incubation Times .... Days

Japanese or Coturnix **Quail** 17-18

Hens and **Bantams** 21

Domestic Duck 28

Call Duck 26

Muscovey Duck 35

Domestic Geese 28-30

Turkey 28

Pheasant (Common) 24-25

Peafowl 28

Guinea Fowl 28

HATCHING

If you incubate in one machine and hatch in another, this allows for more space in the incubator, and is a great help if the eggs are not all due to hatch at the same time.

Put the eggs of different kinds into separate containers when hatching a variety of breeds, particularly if the chicks look the same, for example Cuckoo Maran and Cuckoo Scots Dumpies.

Make sure the sides of the containers are high enough to stop the chicks from clambering out, or use closed containers with ½" inch holes in the top and round the sides. Return the containers to the incubator or hatcher.

Because of the rise in carbon dioxide, caused by the primary respiratory system, the chick makes an involuntary jerk with its neck which in turn causes the beak to rupture the **air sac**. The chick now takes its first gasp of air. The lungs start to fill, the blood circulation goes into overdrive and the chick starts to jerk some more. As is does so, it pierces the shell of the egg. The body of the chick begins to uncoil and rotate causing it to pierce the shell with a series of holes (**pipping**) in an anti-clockwise direction. The final jerk of the body pushes the blunt end of the egg off and the chick's head pops out. Now the feet and legs come into their own, and heave the body out of the shell leaving the chick wet and tired.

It is very important at this stage not to open the incubator. Allow the chicks time to rest and fluff up before investigating.

Once the chicks have fluffed up or dried remove them to the rearing box, see "REARING" on page 48. Caution is necessary here – do not keep opening the incubator to have a look; the length of time for hatching can vary from a few hours to two days. If you keep opening the incubator, you lose the humidity in the machine – let nature take its course.

If many of the chicks have hatched, and others have pipped but have now stopped, you can help them out by breaking open the egg around the area of **pipping**. Be careful, and watch out for any blood vessels – do not break these, as you will kill the chick.

If a chick when hatched, has a messy vent, or has not absorbed the yolk as it should have done, it must be culled: chicks should always be clean. You must be careful to look out for any deformities.

All chicks have an **egg tooth**, on top of the beak at the end, see "Developing chick embryos" on page 43. Without this the chick could not hatch. This 'tooth' falls off a few hours or days after hatching.

SEXING

If you think you are able to sex your chicks by size, weight or looks – you can't! We have had professional sexers at the DFT for a number of years using both visual and endoscopic methods. They are good, but not 100% accurate. In most breeds, the sexes are identical when hatched, but sexing is possible by feather and by colour.

Feather Sexing

Feather sexing is most common in the commercial world where unskilled labour can tell the difference by the shape of the wing feathers.

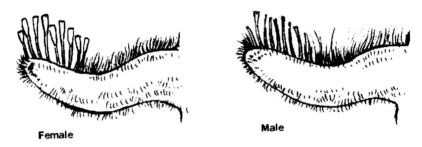

Female   Male

Feather sexing

These birds have been genetically designed to save the cost of using the more expensive professional sexers. (Diagram)

Colour Sexing

Colour sexing comes in three types:

When you cross certain breeds, the colour of the offspring is sex dependent – if you mate a Rhode Island Red cockerel with a Light Sussex hen, the chicks come out red female, white male.

There are some **auto-sexing breeds**, which are basically colour crosses, but have developed a little further. These are Brockbar,

46

Brussbar, Cambar, Dorbar, Legbar, Rhodebar Welbar, Wybar Legbar, etc.

Finally, some breeds do have certain down and feather differences when hatched. These are not always totally reliable, but are to be found in Welsummers, Dorkings, Appenzellers, and Marans to name a few.

Egg Weight

An interesting study has been going on to try to sex chicks by the weight of the egg before incubation. The results so far have been inconclusive.

Effect of Incubation Temperature

Another interesting point is that, during the very hot summers we have been experiencing in the last few years in England, there has always been a larger percentage of male chicks hatched. Studies into certain reptiles, alligators in particular, have shown that a warmer incubation temperature or climate triggers off a mechanism in the embryo to hatch only, or mainly, male young. Is there a connection here with chickens?

REARING

There are two easy methods of rearing in small numbers. It is always best to use dark **heat** instead of infra red bulbs, as chick grow in their sleep and tend to have fewer vices such as toe, shoulder and wing pecking. If you are rearing in the early spring, you may use additional programmed **lighting**: a 40 watt electric bulb for the mornings so that the chicks go to sleep naturally in the evening. It is best to manually turn down the light with a dimmer switch; otherwise the chicks may find themselves left out away from the heat source when the timer turns the light off – this leads to cheepings of protest and crowding in corners, and perhaps death by suffocation.

Find a suitable cardboard box, or make a wooden **rearing box**, approximately 3' long by 2' wide by 1' high. You can keep up to 35 chicks in a box this size. Put in a bed of shavings approximately 1" deep and place the heat source at one end. Put in a pan of fresh chick crumbs, and a one litre plastic chick drinker about 6" away from the heat source. Add some probiotics to the food or water. Dip each chick's beak into the water when you put it into the box, and then place it under the heat.

For the first few days they appear not to bother too much about feeding: this is because when the chick hatches it absorbs its yolk sac through its vent, and can survive the first 48 hours without food. Raise the heat lamp as the chicks grow.

After a week, replace the food pan with a 1 litre chick feeder; the chicks tend to scratch the food out of the pan and waste it. At the same time spray the chicks and container daily with VIRKON S; this helps to control any viruses, or **bacteria** such as E-coli. A sure sign that the chicks are doing well is when they start sparring or fighting.

Clean them out regularly; a dust pan and brush does well.

If you want to **mark the chicks** for identification, mark the head or the legs with a coloured felt tipped pen, or use coloured leg rings. Rings are the best way: be sure to change them as the chick grows – the rings should slide easily up and down the leg.

ELECTRIC HEN

This is suitable for hen, bantam, turkey, pheasants and guinea fowl chicks. It is not suitable for ducks and geese, and must be used indoors, in a heated room.

Adjust the legs of the electric hen: a 1½" gap above the shavings is about right for newly-hatched chicks.

CERAMIC BULB HEATER

This is for water fowl, being warmer, but will do for hen and bantam chicks too.

The heater consists of a 75 watt or 100 watt ceramic bulb, and a procelain bulb holder complete with shade. Use a wire or chain (not the electric flex) to hang the heater approximately 6" above the box. The bottom of the shade may initially be about 1½" above the shavings, but raise the lamp for large goslings to avoid singeing their heads.

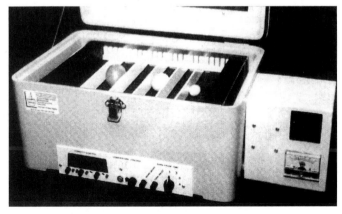

AB incubator

WHERE DID I GO WRONG?

You should not expect miracles – even the commercial hatcheries using modern breeds only get 85% to 90%, and with some pure breeds experts are happy to get 30%.

It is always interesting to know why eggs **fail**, but it is not always that simple to work out why. Please remember there may not be one reason alone, but a mixture of reasons, why these eggs did not hatch, and this makes the diagnosis more complex.

Open the eggs and have a look inside – this can be a messy and smelly process. Remember, **clear eggs** do not smell; eggs only smell if they start developing and then stop – particularly duck and goose eggs. (Remember also that you should have pulled out the eggs that were not developing when candling.)

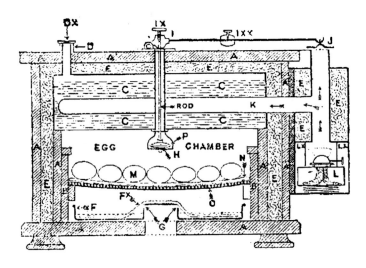

A water tank incubator

CLEAR EGGS

- Cockerel **infertile**; check him for lice and **fleas** and/or change the cockerel.
- Poor storage; eggs were frosted or contaminated.
- Eggs were chilled in the incubator at an early stage. **Power Failure**

EMBRYO DYING AT AN EARLY STAGE

- Fluctuations in **temperature** in incubator, could be too hot or too cold. Check the thermostat or setting of the incubator.
- **Power failure**, eggs were chilled
- Eggs were held in **storage for too long**.
- Hot or cold spot in the incubator.

EMBRYO DYING MID-TERM

- Temperature in incubator too hot or cold. Was the thermometer at the right level?
- Incorrect or poor **turning** programme.
- Build-up of **bacteria** in incubator, due to poor hygiene.
- hot or cold spot in incubator.
- Eggs were held in storage for too long.
- Certain breeds which are very closely bred, have weak embryos – Sebrights & Hamburgs are notorious.
- Eggs damaged during transport.

DEAD IN SHELL

- Too much **humidity**; use less water during the incubation period.
- Too low humidity, add a little extra water during incubation, and/or more water at hatching time.
- A build up of bacteria within the incubator due to poor hygiene.
- Incubator temperature thermostat set too low or too high.
- Incorrect or poor **turning** programme.

OVERDUE HATCHING

- Too low a temperature in incubator, adjust thermostat to next setting.
- Too low humidity at hatching time. Add more water.

EARLY HATCHING

- Temperature too high, adjust thermostat to next setting or adjust thermometer level.
- Eggs held in a **too warm storage** area; premature incubation.

Chick Symptoms

When your chicks have hatched, they may have the following symptoms.

Sticky

Too high or low temperature in incubator and humidity too low. Very often these birds are survivors.

Crooked Toes

Poor diet in breeding stock.

Too high or too low temperature in incubator.

Too bright or hot **brooder** (usually white heat bulb).

No remedy – best to cull.

Splayed Legs

Too smooth surface in incubator.

Rearing on newspaper which is too smooth – use shavings instead.

This can be corrected by tying a woollen strand to both legs for up to 2 weeks.

Star Gazers

These are chicks that stand and stare up at the sky, slightly shaking their heads, cause: **ENCEPHALAMASIA** – cull.

Always ensure that you buy chick crumbs that are within the sell-by date. If you buy them loose (in kilos) ask to see the bag they came from and the storage date on the label; stale food leads to messy bums on chicks.

EGG TRANSMITTED DISEASES

The following diseases are transmitted by egg:

> Adenovirus
> Aspergillosis
> Avian Encephalomyelitis
> Fowl Typhoid
> Infectious Bronchitis
> Infectious synovitis
> Lymphoid Leucosis
> Mycoplasma Gallisepticum
> Mycoplasma Meleagridis

Salmonellae including Pullorum
Yolk Sac Infection

This is so important, that it is illegal to bring hatching eggs into this country!

TIMING

When setting eggs it is important to think about when they are going to hatch, and whether you will have time to be on hand when they do. It may be better for the eggs to hatch at the weekend, on your day off, or during term time, etc., so timing is all important.

An Ecostat incubator

SCHOOL TEACHER, CLASSROOM AND PROJECTS

This chapter is to help school teachers, to ensure that their classroom projects will go well, so this is also a preliminary **check list**.

- You need a reliable source for your hatching eggs – see if you can find some sex-linked ones. Look for adverts in papers and magazines which advertise such as Poultry World, Farmers Weekly, Farmers Guardian from W. H. Smith or Fancy Fowl: telephone (01635) 253239 for a copy.

- Incubators. Some schools have bought their own, some hire them or are loaned them from a central source. Whatever machine you obtain, always go for an automatic turner, (because of weekends) and make sure it works! After this, sterilise it.

- Location is sometimes a problem in classrooms. Place the incubator on a strong table or bench, with twin electric sockets near by. Always tape up the plugs because of cleaners, etc., and protect it from direct sunlight. Do not place it over a radiator. Do not allow children to fiddle with the controls.

- You will need a candler. This you can make up or buy. Battery candlers are about £4.00, mains electric candlers are £12.00–£16.00.

- Lamp or brooders. When your chicks have hatched you will require a rearing box, lamp or electric hen.

- You will need feeders, drinkers, chick crumbs, shavings and VIRKON S. Make sure the chick crumbs are fresh. If they are sold loose, ask to see the bag and check the storage date on it.

- Timing is important: hatch your chicks out at the right moment during the term. Remember about holidays, hatching over weekends, etc. Work backwards from the optimum hatching day.

- What are you going to do with your chicks when the project is finished, and you have kept them for a week or two? You must have someone lined up to take them off your hands, even though the majority might be cockerels.

There are a number of projects that you can do during incubation and after hatching. Here are some detailed below:

- Plot the growth of the air sac.
- Check the weight loss of the egg during incubation.
- Record the temperature inside and outside the incubator.
- Record the humidity inside and outside the incubator.
- Weigh each egg, mark and weigh each chick and compare.
- Record weight gain of each chick.

With the best will in the world, there are always going to be failures, so do not encourage your children to expect too much. Be pleasantly surprised at your successes!

A Lyon Electric Co. Turn-X Model TX6

INDEX

THE EGYPTIAN EXPERIENCE

In the days of the Egyptian Pharaohs the flesh of the hyena was considered such a delicacy that these animals were force-fed on ducks and geese! Although this practice died out a long time ago, there are still legacies to be found from the ancient times in Egypt which the tourist rarely comes across.

One of these is the method of incubating hens' eggs in vast numbers which was perfected by the Egyptians during the last Dynastic period about 300 BC, some 1,000 years after the chicken was introduced into Egypt from India via Mesopotamia. Evidence of the chicken's arrival in Egypt comes from the restored 'Annals' of Tuthmosis III at Karnak as translated by Kurt Sethe where he mentions "four birds that bear every day" (dated about 1450 BC). When Howard Carter was excavating in the Valley of the Kings with Lord Carnarvon he found an ostracon, or flake of limestone, with a drawing of a cockerel on it which he dated at somewhere around 1300 BC. A silver bowl from the time of Seti II (about 1210 BC) provides another clue with a cockerel and two young birds in a farmyard scene, while a limestone relief from the tomb of Hapiu (about 360 BC) depicts a harpist with a splendid cockerel at his feet. As we move into the Greco-Roman period, 332 BC to 30 AD, much more evidence appears, not only on papyrus and limestone reliefs, but also on pottery. Diodorus Siculus, the historian living at the time of Augustus (63 BC – 14 AD) wrote that the Egyptians were artificially incubating eggs on a large scale.

It is interesting to note that no cockerels or hens were used in hieroglyphs, although one character depicting a quail has been confused with a chick. Ducks, geese and pigeons were produced in vast quantities during Pharaonic times as can be seen in many bas-reliefs, particularly in Saqqara, south of Cairo. This experience was transferred to chickens once they had become more common-place, with the result that, owing to the efficiency of the ancient method of incubation, the breeds that exist today are non-sitters.

The incubator man shuffles across the floor of the incubator room. There are some 5000 eggs on the floor. As he moves across the floor he feels and listens to the eggs.

The eggs are turned every 4 hours. Eggs are often piled up, and turning is entirely random.

The large scale incubation method in Egypt originated from the simple bread oven which was made of mud bricks mixed with rice straw. So successful were these ovens that the Egyptians adapted the idea and built special incubator buildings capable of hatching thousands of eggs. These buildings were constructed of mud brick and straw with a central passageway and alcoves on either side. The alcoves could hold from 1,000 to 5,000 eggs, and were divided horizontally with a floor about waist height to contain the eggs, and a rice straw fire below. At the entrance to the building would be the incubator man's living quarters; this was a family affair, and the specialised knowledge of incubation was handed down from father to son.

The incubator man was able to sense if any alcove was too warm or too cool and could raise or lower the temperature by adjusting the fire. He would test the temperature of the eggs by rolling them with his hands and holding each one to his eye lid; an infertile egg doesn't hold its heat. He was also able to test for cracked shells or dead embryos by holding the eggs to his ear and "listening" to them. The eggs were set out randomly on reed matting, and were rolled and checked every four hours and candled daily, hence the need for the family to live on site. In ancient times candling was done by using a shaft of light through a hole in the roof of the building, but these days a wooden box with a bright light inside is used instead. Candling is the method of checking the embryo's development inside the egg, and it is called that because, in the old days before electricity, candles were used to look through the egg in a darkened room.

There is still at least one family left using the ancient system of incubation today, and we visited them at their farm on the outskirts of an oasis town south of Cairo. The incubator building was constructed of bricks and cement but the system was basically the same as in the days of the Pharaohs, except that oil lamps were used instead of fires to provide the heat. It was quite something to see 5,000 eggs laid out on a mat, and even more so when the chicks started to hatch! Of the 5,000 eggs incubated, about 4,2000 chicks came out. I would attribute this percentage of hatch to either too much or too little turning, as this system is entirely random. One of the most interesting points is that no thermometers or any equipment are ever used. (Chickens take 21 days to incubate and hatch.)

Each incubator room was 3 metres x 3 metres x 90 centimetres high (10 feet x 10 feet x 3 feet high) with an access door in the front of 60 centimetres x 60 centimetres (2 feet x 2 feet). The floor was first covered with several centimetres of chopped rice straw and levelled, and then a fine reed mat was laid on top. These incubator rooms had an upstairs but separate counterpart, with access not only from outside but also via a trap door in the centre of the floor. Up to nine paraffin lamps were placed on the floor, mainly round the walls and in the corners, and these were gradually reduced to 4 or 5 as incubation continued. The lamps would die down as the oxygen in the room decreased, but they would be checked every four hours and adjusted when necessary.

Because the incubator that we saw was built close to the ground and not far from an irrigation canal, the eggs had enough humidity to hatch without any additional water, but in the very hot summer months they are sprayed with water from the 15th day. When the chicks hatch the doors are opened and they pour out towards the light into special floor areas where they are fed and watered for a day or two before being dispatched to the customers. After the hatch the incubator rooms are cleared of shells and unhatched eggs, the matting is removed, the rice straw swept up, and the whole area is disinfected. This was done by fire in the old days, and all the alcoves were torched with straw.

It is not at all certain how many other traditional incubators are still working in Egypt, but it seems that we may well have visited one of the last; the family owned in addition two very large Dutch automatic incubators which they used in the busier season during the summer, and they seemed to imply that hatches were better with the modern method, so I would think that it is only a matter of time before the traditional system dies out.